Contents

Instructions

This book is designed for children who are beginning to gain numerical confidence. Children should **not** attempt this book until they have reached ANT standard in the previous books in the series, dedicated to these specific times tables, or are able to recite the table with minimal hesitation.

The book follows the principles of the Numberella Maths Training series - goal and reward focused exercises, presented on a beautiful, symmetrical template, which children enjoy working on, and coming back to.

There are four different types of skill sets, A, B, C and Medley. Each exercise requires the child to complete a different part of a question – rather than only the answer – and thus builds a complete numerical framework within their brain. Furthermore, answers are written on the letter 'x' which introduces from an early age the idea that a letter can be a number – the basis of algebra.

By weaving the different times tables together, in the A B C Medley system described above, the child begins to develop 'Three Way' thinking – meaning that they begin to be able to manage multiple options simultaneously. Acquiring this skill is critical to their ability to solve problems. As they acclimatize to the demands of the exercises, the child's brain will get used to 'Three Way Thinking', and they will begin to develop a 'Power Brain.'

It is paramount that goal setting, prize giving, and graph plotting take place. This process embeds the principal that practice equals improvement, and will give your child a healthy work ethic, based on self-belief.

As a child becomes more confident around numbers, they should be encouraged to work on their speed. The goal of all books in the Numberella Maths Training series is to bring children to ANT level – where their brains begin to process numbers automatically, and effortlessly. With arithmetic thus transformed, the child's brain is free to focus on word processing and problem solving, which will form the core of their ability to tackle more complex maths questions as they move forward in the syllabus.

Used with patience and persistence, this book will help your child build a solid and lasting foundation on which to base their entire mathematical construct.

Alexander F.L. Newberry
MSt. Oxon
Numberella Founder

Instructions

1) Instruct child to fill in the date. If they don't, they won't be eligible for their 5 second exercise bonus.

2) Instruct them to set their goal. Allow them to set whatever goal they like. They must set a goal to get the 5 second exercise bonus.

3) As long as they are confident, time them completing the exercise.

4) Once they have finished, stop the clock and ask them to check their work for mistakes. (Such as writing numbers the wrong way round or getting a wrong answer.)

5) Once they have checked, write their time down, and reward them with their 5 second bonus, and whatever big sticker prize they have won. Make a show of the prize giving to make them feel good.

6) If they have achieved their goal or set a Personal Best, they can stick a Goal/PB sticker onto Antonio's eyes, thus making Antonio's face complete. You should encourage them to do this.

7) Plot their time on the graphs in the back of the book. If you practice daily, after time, the graph will show great improvement. Use the visual aid to prove to them that they can get better.

8) Young children learning numbers often have short attention spans. They will probably only manage 1 exercise at a time, but if they are keen to try more, let them.

9) Never force the issue. Be patient. If they don't want to do it, they lack confidence, or sufficient incentive. Work to build their confidence by establishing a better method, give them an exciting incentive (pocket money is great) or consider moving to an easier level.

Skill Set A

Circle your goal. Fill in the numbers in the 'A' Column. If you write the date and get 100% you get a 5 second bonus!

Medals & Prizes!

Make Antonio by setting a Personal Best, reaching your goal, and winning a medal.

ANT	20
Gold	30
Silver	50
Bronze	01:30
Hand Speed	
Bonus	
Total Time	

ANTONIO

P * B   GOAL

Question	A		B		C
1	X	+	1	=	20
2	X	+	5	=	20
3	X	+	15	=	20
4	X	+	19	=	20
5	X	+	9	=	20
6	X	+	3	=	20
7	X	+	19	=	20
8	X	+	16	=	20
9	X	+	0	=	20
10	X	+	7	=	20
11	X	+	2	=	20
12	X	+	1	=	20
13	X	+	19	=	20
14	X	+	5	=	20
15	X	+	7	=	20
16	X	+	11	=	20
17	X	+	12	=	20
18	X	+	3	=	20
19	X	+	12	=	20
20	X	+	10	=	20

Circle your goal. Fill in the numbers in the 'B' Column. If you write the date and get 100% you get a 5 second bonus!

Question	A		B		C	Medals & Prizes!
	19	+	x	=	20	
	13	+	x	=	20	Make Antonio by setting a Personal Best, reaching your goal, and winning a medal.
	8	+	x	=	20	
	0	+	x	=	20	20 — ANT
	9	+	x	=	20	
	15	+	x	=	20	30 — Gold
	5	+	x	=	20	
	11	+	x	=	20	50 — Silver
	13	+	x	=	20	
	3	+	x	=	20	01:30 — Bronze
	11	+	x	=	20	Hand Speed
	18	+	x	=	20	Bonus
	12	+	x	=	20	Total Time
	18	+	x	=	20	ANTONIO
	16	+	x	=	20	P * B GOAL
	14	+	x	=	20	
	2	+	x	=	20	
	17	+	x	=	20	
	11	+	x	=	20	
	0	+	x	=	20	

Circle your goal. Fill in the numbers in the 'C' Column. Check your answers. If you write the date and get 100% you get a 5 second bonus!

Medals & Prizes!

Make Antonio by setting a Personal Best, reaching your goal, and winning a medal.

ANT	20	
Gold	30	
Silver	50	
Bronze	01:30	
Hand Speed		
Bonus		
Total Time		

ANTONIO

P * B   GOAL

Question	A		B		C
1	12	+	3	=	x
2	12	+	5	=	x
3	0	+	5	=	x
4	3	+	9	=	x
5	3	+	4	=	x
6	9	+	3	=	x
7	6	+	2	=	x
8	3	+	1	=	x
9	12	+	3	=	x
10	4	+	1	=	x
11	5	+	11	=	x
12	7	+	5	=	x
13	8	+	2	=	x
14	1	+	11	=	x
15	7	+	11	=	x
16	5	+	7	=	x
17	12	+	7	=	x
18	11	+	3	=	x
19	11	+	3	=	x
20	5	+	8	=	x

Skill Set Medley

Circle your goal. Fill in the numbers iin the boxes marked 'X'. Check your answers. If you write the date and get 100% you get a 5 second bonus!

Question	A		B		C
	X	+	13	=	20
	4	+	X	=	20
	12	+	9	=	X
	17	+	X	=	20
	X	+	2	=	20
	10	+	X	=	20
	7	+	8	=	X
	2	+	X	=	20
	X	+	20	=	20
	1	+	X	=	20
	5	+	3	=	X
	3	+	X	=	20
	X	+	7	=	20
	19	+	X	=	20
	7	+	7	=	X
	7	+	X	=	20
	X	+	19	=	20
	15	+	X	=	20
	12	+	4	=	X
	19	+	X	=	20

Medals & Prizes!

Make Antonio by setting a Personal Best, reaching your goal, and winning a medal.

20	ANT
30	Gold
50	Silver
01:30	Bronze
	Hand Speed
	Bonus
	Total Time

ANTONIO

P * B   GOAL

Date	Skill Set A		Ex.	5

Question	A		B		C
	x	+	2	=	20
	x	+	17	=	20
	x	+	6	=	20
	x	+	4	=	20
	x	+	3	=	20
	x	+	5	=	20
	x	+	20	=	20
	x	+	12	=	20
	x	+	11	=	20
	x	+	6	=	20
	x	+	16	=	20
	x	+	17	=	20
	x	+	4	=	20
	x	+	10	=	20
	x	+	2	=	20
	x	+	13	=	20
	x	+	13	=	20
	x	+	1	=	20
	x	+	3	=	20
	x	+	1	=	20

Medals & Prizes!

Make Antonio by setting a Personal Best, reaching your goal, and winning a medal.

ANT	20
Gold	30
Silver	50
Bronze	01:30
Hand Speed	
Bonus	
Total Time	

ANTONIO

P * B   GOAL

Ex.	6	Skill Set B				Date (to qualify for bonus)

Circle your goal. Fill in the numbers in the 'B' Column. If you write the date and get 100% you get a 5 second bonus!

Question	A		B		C	Medals & Prizes!
	17	+	x	=	20	Make Antonio by setting a Personal Best, reaching your goal, and winning a medal.
	19	+	x	=	20	
	6	+	x	=	20	
	8	+	x	=	20	20 ANT
	0	+	x	=	20	
	16	+	x	=	20	30 Gold
	15	+	x	=	20	
	16	+	x	=	20	50 Silver
	1	+	x	=	20	
	6	+	x	=	20	01:30 Bronze
	7	+	x	=	20	Hand Speed
	17	+	x	=	20	Bonus
	11	+	x	=	20	Total Time
	11	+	x	=	20	ANTONIO
	14	+	x	=	20	P * B GOAL
	9	+	x	=	20	
	16	+	x	=	20	
	5	+	x	=	20	
	7	+	x	=	20	
	5	+	x	=	20	

| Date | Skill Set C | | Ex. | 7 |

Circle your goal. Fill in the numbers in the 'C' Column. Check your answers. If you write the date and get 100% you get a 5 second bonus!

Medals & Prizes!

Make Antonio by setting a Personal Best, reaching your goal, and winning a medal.

ANT	20	
Gold	30	
Silver	50	
Bronze	01:30	
Hand Speed		
Bonus		
Total Time		

ANTONIO

P * B   GOAL

Question	A		B		C
1	3	+	12	=	x
2	2	+	8	=	x
3	3	+	3	=	x
4	1	+	11	=	x
5	7	+	6	=	x
6	8	+	10	=	x
7	1	+	9	=	x
8	5	+	4	=	x
9	8	+	0	=	x
10	10	+	2	=	x
11	10	+	6	=	x
12	4	+	9	=	x
13	6	+	0	=	x
14	6	+	10	=	x
15	1	+	12	=	x
16	8	+	11	=	x
17	5	+	0	=	x
18	1	+	8	=	x
19	0	+	5	=	x
20	0	+	2	=	x

Ex.	8	Skill Set Medley		Date

Question	A		B		C
	X	+	10	=	20
	11	+	X	=	20
	9	+	9	=	X
	4	+	X	=	20
	X	+	20	=	20
	13	+	X	=	20
	10	+	6	=	X
	20	+	X	=	20
	X	+	7	=	20
	20	+	X	=	20
	0	+	0	=	X
	8	+	X	=	20
	X	+	19	=	20
	0	+	X	=	20
	3	+	0	=	X
	19	+	X	=	20
	X	+	13	=	20
	8	+	X	=	20
	10	+	4	=	X
	13	+	X	=	20

Medals & Prizes!

Make Antonio by setting a Personal Best, reaching your goal, and winning a medal.

20	ANT
30	Gold
50	Silver
01:30	Bronze
	Hand Speed
	Bonus
	Total Time

ANTONIO

P * B   GOAL

11

Circle your goal. Fill in the numbers in the 'A' Column. If you write the date and get 100% you get a 5 second bonus!

Medals & Prizes!

Make Antonio by setting a Personal Best, reaching your goal, and winning a medal.

ANT	20
Gold	30
Silver	50
Bronze	01:30
Hand Speed	
Bonus	
Total Time	

ANTONIO
P * B   GOAL

Question	A		B		C
1	X	+	1	=	20
2	X	+	12	=	20
3	X	+	9	=	20
4	X	+	19	=	20
5	X	+	3	=	20
6	X	+	3	=	20
7	X	+	9	=	20
8	X	+	5	=	20
9	X	+	20	=	20
10	X	+	10	=	20
11	X	+	17	=	20
12	X	+	18	=	20
13	X	+	5	=	20
14	X	+	18	=	20
15	X	+	7	=	20
16	X	+	9	=	20
17	X	+	14	=	20
18	X	+	7	=	20
19	X	+	7	=	20
20	X	+	17	=	20

Ex.	10	Skill Set B				Date

Question	A		B		C	Medals & Prizes!
	10	+	x	=	20	
	20	+	x	=	20	Make Antonio by setting a Personal Best, reaching your goal, and winning a medal.
	4	+	x	=	20	
	1	+	x	=	20	20 ANT
	3	+	x	=	20	
	16	+	x	=	20	30 Gold
	0	+	x	=	20	
	8	+	x	=	20	50 Silver
	11	+	x	=	20	
	2	+	x	=	20	01:30 Bronze
	8	+	x	=	20	Hand Speed
	10	+	x	=	20	Bonus
	20	+	x	=	20	Total Time
	12	+	x	=	20	ANTONIO
	7	+	x	=	20	P * B GOAL
	16	+	x	=	20	
	15	+	x	=	20	
	7	+	x	=	20	
	14	+	x	=	20	
	10	+	x	=	20	

Circle your goal. Fill in the numbers in the 'C' Column. Check your answers. If you write the date and get 100% you get a 5 second bonus!

Medals & Prizes!

Make Antonio by setting a Personal Best, reaching your goal, and winning a medal.

ANT	20
Gold	30
Silver	50
Bronze	01:30
Hand Speed	
Bonus	
Total Time	

ANTONIO

P * B   GOAL

Question	A		B		C
1	5	+	2	=	X
2	12	+	6	=	X
3	12	+	6	=	X
4	8	+	12	=	X
5	0	+	3	=	X
6	1	+	3	=	X
7	8	+	3	=	X
8	9	+	0	=	X
9	7	+	2	=	X
10	9	+	7	=	X
11	5	+	11	=	X
12	10	+	1	=	X
13	3	+	6	=	X
14	3	+	3	=	X
15	5	+	3	=	X
16	8	+	2	=	X
17	5	+	6	=	X
18	11	+	9	=	X
19	3	+	4	=	X
20	2	+	4	=	X

| Ex. | 12 | Skill Set Medley | | | | Date |

Circle your goal. Fill in the numbers iin the boxes marked 'X'. Check your answers. If you write the date and get 100% you get a 5 second bonus!

Question	A		B		C	Medals & Prizes!
	X	+	1	=	20	
	7	+	X	=	20	Make Antonio by setting a Personal Best, reaching your goal, and winning a medal.
	0	+	5	=	X	
	12	+	X	=	20	20 · ANT
	X	+	17	=	20	
	17	+	X	=	20	· 30 · Gold
	1	+	6	=	X	
	17	+	X	=	20	50 · Silver
	X	+	19	=	20	
	0	+	X	=	20	01:30 · Bronze
	11	+	12	=	X	
	9	+	X	=	20	Hand Speed
	X	+	4	=	20	Bonus
	18	+	X	=	20	Total Time
	8	+	8	=	X	ANTONIO
	4	+	X	=	20	P * B GOAL
	X	+	3	=	20	
	2	+	X	=	20	
	0	+	7	=	X	
	3	+	X	=	20	

Circle your goal. Fill in the numbers in the 'A' Column. If you write the date and get 100% you get a 5 second bonus!

Medals & Prizes!

Make Antonio by setting a Personal Best, reaching your goal, and winning a medal.

ANT	20
Gold	30
Silver	50
Bronze	01:30
Hand Speed	
Bonus	
Total Time	

ANTONIO

P * B	GOAL

Question	A		B		C
	x	+	1	=	20
	x	+	18	=	20
	x	+	18	=	20
	x	+	20	=	20
	x	+	3	=	20
	x	+	15	=	20
	x	+	13	=	20
	x	+	12	=	20
	x	+	14	=	20
	x	+	2	=	20
	x	+	10	=	20
	x	+	0	=	20
	x	+	0	=	20
	x	+	12	=	20
15	x	+	16	=	20
16	x	+	18	=	20
17	x	+	4	=	20
18	x	+	8	=	20
19	x	+	15	=	20
20	x	+	4	=	20

Ex.	14	Skill Set B				

Circle your goal. Fill in the numbers in the 'B' Column. If you write the date and get 100% you get a 5 second bonus!

Question	A		B		C	
	5	+	x	=	20	**Medals & Prizes!**
	11	+	x	=	20	Make Antonio by setting a Personal Best, reaching your goal, and winning a medal.
	16	+	x	=	20	
	12	+	x	=	20	20 ANT
	15	+	x	=	20	
	2	+	x	=	20	30 Gold
	13	+	x	=	20	
	13	+	x	=	20	50 Silver
	15	+	x	=	20	
	2	+	x	=	20	01:30 Bronze
	18	+	x	=	20	Hand Speed
	11	+	x	=	20	Bonus
	13	+	x	=	20	Total Time
	6	+	x	=	20	ANTONIO
	14	+	x	=	20	P * B GOAL
	20	+	x	=	20	
	8	+	x	=	20	
	16	+	x	=	20	
	12	+	x	=	20	
	18	+	x	=	20	

Circle your goal. Fill in the numbers in the 'C' Column. Check your answers. If you write the date and get 100% you get a 5 second bonus!

Medals & Prizes!		Question	A		B		C
Make Antonio by setting a Personal Best, reaching your goal, and winning a medal.		1	8	+	10	=	X
		2	1	+	5	=	X
ANT	20	3	11	+	9	=	X
		4	4	+	10	=	X
Gold	30	5	1	+	3	=	X
		6	2	+	5	=	X
Silver	50	7	9	+	11	=	X
		8	10	+	7	=	X
Bronze	01:30	9	5	+	0	=	X
		10	3	+	11	=	X
Hand Speed		11	5	+	6	=	X
Bonus		12	7	+	0	=	X
Total Time		13	5	+	10	=	X
ANTONIO		14	1	+	5	=	X
P * B GOAL		15	7	+	1	=	X
		16	9	+	3	=	X
		17	7	+	7	=	X
		18	4	+	1	=	X
		19	11	+	5	=	X
		20	8	+	4	=	X

Ex.	16	Skill Set Medley				Date

Circle your goal. Fill in the numbers iin the boxes marked 'X'. Check your answers. If you write the date and get 100% you get a 5 second bonus!

Question	A		B		C
	X	+	16	=	20
	12	+	X	=	20
	10	+	0	=	X
	4	+	X	=	20
	X	+	19	=	20
	10	+	X	=	20
	0	+	9	=	X
	19	+	X	=	20
	X	+	11	=	20
	2	+	X	=	20
	9	+	3	=	X
	1	+	X	=	20
	X	+	6	=	20
	13	+	X	=	20
	0	+	0	=	X
	6	+	X	=	20
	X	+	0	=	20
	10	+	X	=	20
	6	+	12	=	X
	0	+	X	=	20

Medals & Prizes!

Make Antonio by setting a Personal Best, reaching your goal, and winning a medal.

20	ANT
30	Gold
50	Silver
01:30	Bronze
	Hand Speed
	Bonus
	Total Time

ANTONIO

P * B   GOAL

Circle your goal. Fill in the numbers in the 'A' Column. If you write the date and get 100% you get a 5 second bonus!

Medals & Prizes!

Make Antonio by setting a Personal Best, reaching your goal, and winning a medal.

		Question	A		B		C
ANT	20		x	+	4	=	20
			x	+	11	=	20
Gold	30		x	+	4	=	20
			x	+	14	=	20
			x	+	6	=	20
Silver	50		x	+	1	=	20
			x	+	15	=	20
			x	+	15	=	20
Bronze	01:30		x	+	20	=	20
			x	+	11	=	20
Hand Speed			x	+	15	=	20
Bonus			x	+	16	=	20
Total Time			x	+	14	=	20
ANTONIO			x	+	11	=	20
P * B GOAL			x	+	14	=	20
			x	+	10	=	20
			x	+	11	=	20
			x	+	14	=	20
			x	+	3	=	20
			x	+	19	=	20

Circle your goal. Fill in the numbers in the 'B' Column. If you write the date and get 100% you get a 5 second bonus!

Question	A		B		C
	7	+	x	=	20
	12	+	x	=	20
	11	+	x	=	20
	7	+	x	=	20
	14	+	x	=	20
	20	+	x	=	20
	14	+	x	=	20
	14	+	x	=	20
	10	+	x	=	20
	0	+	x	=	20
	14	+	x	=	20
	10	+	x	=	20
	3	+		=	20
	0	+	x	=	20
	20	+	x	=	20
	1	+	x	=	20
	6	+	x	=	20
	7	+	x	=	20
	2	+	x	=	20
	14	+		=	20

Medals & Prizes!

Make Antonio by setting a Personal Best, reaching your goal, and winning a medal.

20	ANT
30	Gold
50	Silver
01:30	Bronze
	Hand Speed
	Bonus
	Total Time

ANTONIO

P * B   GOAL

Date			

Circle your goal. Fill in the numbers in the 'C' Column. Check your answers. If you write the date and get 100% you get a 5 second bonus!

Medals & Prizes!

Make Antonio by setting a Personal Best, reaching your goal, and winning a medal.

ANT	20
Gold	30
Silver	50
Bronze	01:30

Hand Speed	
Bonus	
Total Time	

ANTONIO

P * B   GOAL

Question	A		B		C
1	2	+	12	=	X
2	4	+	10	=	X
3	7	+	6	=	X
4	1	+	10	=	X
5	4	+	11	=	X
6	1	+	7	=	X
7	5	+	9	=	X
8	4	+	1	=	X
9	0	+	9	=	X
10	7	+	0	=	X
11	0	+	10	=	X
12	5	+	5	=	X
13	9	+	8	=	X
14	9	+	3	=	X
15	0	+	1	=	X
16	1	+	6	=	X
17	8	+	4	=	X
18	8	+	7	=	X
19	12	+	2	=	X
20	7	+	6	=	X

Skill Set Medley

Circle your goal. Fill in the numbers iin the boxes marked 'X'. Check your answers. If you write the date and get 100% you get a 5 second bonus!

Question	A		B		C
	X	+	12	=	20
	6	+	X	=	20
	1	+	7	=	X
	7	+	X	=	20
	X	+	1	=	20
	19	+	X	=	20
	7	+	0	=	X
	1	+	X	=	20
	X	+	8	=	20
	1	+	X	=	20
	10	+	2	=	X
	7	+	X	=	20
	X	+	12	=	20
	3	+	X	=	20
	4	+	9	=	X
	12	+	X	=	20
	X	+	15	=	20
	13	+	X	=	20
	7	+	0	=	X
	15	+	X	=	20

Medals & Prizes!

Make Antonio by setting a Personal Best, reaching your goal, and winning a medal.

20	ANT
30	Gold
50	Silver
01:30	Bronze
	Hand Speed
	Bonus
	Total Time

ANTONIO

P * B   GOAL

Circle your goal. Fill in the numbers in the 'A' Column. If you write the date and get 100% you get a 5 second bonus!

Medals & Prizes!

Make Antonio by setting a Personal Best, reaching your goal, and winning a medal.

ANT	20
Gold	30
Silver	50
Bronze	01:30
Hand Speed	
Bonus	
Total Time	

ANTONIO

P * B   GOAL

Question	A			B		C
	x	+		10	=	20
	x	+		11	=	20
	x	+		12	=	20
	x	+		17	=	20
	x	+		13	=	20
	x	+		7	=	20
	x	+		0	=	20
	x	+		16	=	20
	x	+		8	=	20
	x	+		11	=	20
	x	+		11	=	20
	x	+		5	=	20
	x	+		1	=	20
	x	+		0	=	20
	x	+		18	=	20
	x	+		4	=	20
	x	+		19	=	20
	x	+		0	=	20
	x	+		0	=	20
	x	+		19	=	20

Ex.	22	Skill Set B					Date

Circle your goal. Fill in the numbers in the 'B' Column. If you write the date and get 100% you get a 5 second bonus!

Question	A		B		C	Medals & Prizes!	
	7	+	X	=	20		
	20	+	X	=	20	Make Antonio by setting a Personal Best, reaching your goal, and winning a medal.	
	5	+	X	=	20		
	12	+	X	=	20	20	ANT
	1	+	X	=	20		
	17	+	X	=	20	30	Gold
	8	+	X	=	20		
	7	+	X	=	20	50	Silver
	2	+	X	=	20		
	17	+	X	=	20	01:30	Bronze
	9	+	X	=	20		Hand Speed
	9	+	X	=	20		Bonus
	17	+	X	=	20		Total Time
	12	+	X	=	20	ANTONIO	
	20	+	X	=	20	P * B	GOAL
	7	+	X	=	20		
	3	+	X	=	20		
	9	+	X	=	20		
	3	+	X	=	20		
	1	+	X	=	20		

Circle your goal. Fill in the numbers in the 'C' Column. Check your answers. If you write the date and get 100% you get a 5 second bonus!

Medals & Prizes!

Make Antonio by setting a Personal Best, reaching your goal, and winning a medal.

ANT	20
Gold	30
Silver	50
Bronze	01:30
Hand Speed	
Bonus	
Total Time	

ANTONIO

P * B   GOAL

Question	A		B		C
1	4	+	10	=	X
2	4	+	2	=	X
3	7	+	8	=	X
4	6	+	1	=	X
5	0	+	2	=	X
6	1	+	6	=	X
7	11	+	7	=	X
8	7	+	4	=	X
9	10	+	1	=	X
10	9	+	0	=	X
11	0	+	9	=	X
12	7	+	9	=	X
13	11	+	4	=	X
14	9	+	4	=	X
15	1	+	11	=	X
16	5	+	2	=	X
17	3	+	7	=	X
18	9	+	1	=	X
19	12	+	1	=	X
20	2	+	0	=	X

Skill Set Medley

Circle your goal. Fill in the numbers iin the boxes marked 'X'. Check your answers. If you write the date and get 100% you get a 5 second bonus!

Question	A		B		C
	X	+	4	=	20
	19	+	X	=	20
	5	+	1	=	X
	12	+	X	=	20
	X	+	1	=	20
	17	+	X	=	20
	2	+	6	=	X
	1	+	X	=	20
	X	+	11	=	20
	16	+	X	=	20
	6	+	2	=	X
	1	+	X	=	20
	X	+	19	=	20
	12	+	X	=	20
	6	+	1	=	X
	19	+	X	=	20
	X	+	5	=	20
	7	+	X	=	20
	6	+	3	=	X
	5	+	X	=	20

Medals & Prizes!

Make Antonio by setting a Personal Best, reaching your goal, and winning a medal.

20	ANT
30	Gold
50	Silver
01:30	Bronze
	Hand Speed
	Bonus
	Total Time

ANTONIO

P * B   GOAL

Circle your goal. Fill in the numbers in the 'A' Column. If you write the date and get 100% you get a 5 second bonus!

Medals & Prizes!

Make Antonio by setting a Personal Best, reaching your goal, and winning a medal.

ANT	20
Gold	30
Silver	50
Bronze	01:30
Hand Speed	
Bonus	
Total Time	

ANTONIO

P * B   GOAL

Question	A		B		C
	x	+	6	=	20
	x	+	0	=	20
	x	+	16	=	20
	x	+	2	=	20
	x	+	5	=	20
	x	+	2	=	20
	x	+	14	=	20
	x	+	8	=	20
	x	+	8	=	20
	x	+	14	=	20
	x	+	2	=	20
	x	+	8	=	20
	x	+	12	=	20
	x	+	13	=	20
	x	+	20	=	20
	x	+	7	=	20
	x	+	3	=	20
	x	+	4	=	20
	x	+	2	=	20
	x	+	20	=	20

Ex.	26	Skill Set B					Date

Circle your goal. Fill in the numbers in the 'B' Column. If you write the date and get 100% you get a 5 second bonus!

Question	A		B			C	Medals & Prizes!
	6	+	X	=		20	
	12	+	X	=		20	Make Antonio by setting a Personal Best, reaching your goal, and winning a medal.
	3	+	X	=		20	
	11	+	X	=		20	20 — ANT
	19	+	X	=		20	
	12	+	X	=		20	30 — Gold
	1	+	X	=		20	
	0	+	X	=		20	50 — Silver
	0	+	X	=		20	
	14	+	X	=		20	01:30 — Bronze
	10	+	X	=		20	Hand Speed
	1	+	X	=		20	Bonus
	12	+	X	=		20	Total Time
	0	+	X	=		20	ANTONIO
	15	+	X	=		20	P * B — GOAL
	5	+	X	=		20	
	12	+	X	=		20	
	11	+	X	=		20	
	5	+	X	=		20	
	17	+	X	=		20	

| | Skill Set C | | Ex. | 27 |

Circle your goal. Fill in the numbers in the 'C' Column. Check your answers. If you write the date and get 100% you get a 5 second bonus!

Medals & Prizes!

Make Antonio by setting a Personal Best, reaching your goal, and winning a medal.

ANT	20
Gold	30
Silver	50
Bronze	01:30
Hand Speed	
Bonus	
Total Time	

ANTONIO
P * B   GOAL

Question	A		B		C
1	0	+	7	=	
2	9	+	9	=	
3	10	+	6	=	
4	5	+	10	=	
5	10	+	0	=	
6	10	+	0	=	
7	11	+	12	=	
8	2	+	7	=	
9	11	+	9	=	
10	11	+	6	=	
11	10	+	1	=	
12	5	+	5	=	
13	11	+	9	=	
14	3	+	11	=	
15	4	+	5	=	
16	0	+	9	=	
17	3	+	10	=	
18	10	+	5	=	
19	6	+	1	=	
20	5	+	9	=	

Circle your goal. Fill in the numbers iin the boxes marked 'X'. Check your answers. If you write the date and get 100% you get a 5 second bonus!

Question	A		B		C
	X	+	4	=	20
	13	+	X	=	20
	1	+	12	=	X
	16	+	X	=	20
	X	+	14	=	20
	3	+	X	=	20
	0	+	1	=	X
	14	+	X	=	20
	X	+	6	=	20
	2	+	X	=	20
	12	+	10	=	X
	5	+	X	=	20
	X	+	15	=	20
	18	+	X	=	20
	12	+	0	=	X
	15	+	X	=	20
	X	+	13	=	20
	20	+	X	=	20
	9	+	5	=	X
	13	+	X	=	20

Medals & Prizes!

Make Antonio by setting a Personal Best, reaching your goal, and winning a medal.

20	ANT
30	Gold
50	Silver
01:30	Bronze
	Hand Speed
	Bonus
	Total Time

ANTONIO

P * B   GOAL

Skill Set A

Circle your goal. Fill in the numbers in the 'A' Column. If you write the date and get 100% you get a 5 second bonus!

Medals & Prizes!

Make Antonio by setting a Personal Best, reaching your goal, and winning a medal.

ANT	20
Gold	30
Silver	50
Bronze	01:30
Hand Speed	
Bonus	
Total Time	

ANTONIO

P * B   GOAL

Question	A		B		C
	X	+	6	=	20
	X	+	13	=	20
	X	+	0	=	20
	X	+	5	=	20
	X	+	13	=	20
	X	+	15	=	20
	X	+	18	=	20
	X	+	13	=	20
	X	+	7	=	20
	X	+	17	=	20
	X	+	4	=	20
	X	+	6	=	20
	X	+	4	=	20
	X	+	15	=	20
	X	+	2	=	20
	X	+	4	=	20
	X	+	3	=	20
	X	+	3	=	20
	X	+	12	=	20
	X	+	1	=	20

Ex.	30	Skill Set B					Date

Circle your goal. Fill in the numbers in the 'B' Column. If you write the date and get 100% you get a 5 second bonus!

Question	A		B		C	Medals & Prizes!	
	0	+	x	=	20		
	5	+	x	=	20	Make Antonio by setting a Personal Best, reaching your goal, and winning a medal.	
	16	+	x	=	20		
	8	+	x	=	20	20	ANT
	11	+	x	=	20		
	11	+	x	=	20	30	Gold
	0	+	x	=	20		
	18	+	x	=	20	50	Silver
	0	+	x	=	20		
	12	+	x	=	20	01:30	Bronze
	19	+	x	=	20	Hand Speed	
	10	+	x	=	20	Bonus	
	14	+	x	=	20	Total Time	
	15	+	x	=	20	ANTONIO	
	1	+	x	=	20	P * B	GOAL
	2	+	x	=	20		
	14	+	x	=	20		
	4	+	x	=	20		
	9	+	x	=	20		
	12	+	x	=	20		

Date		Skill Set C				Ex.	31

Circle your goal. Fill in the numbers in the 'C' Column. Check your answers. If you write the date and get 100% you get a 5 second bonus!

	Question	A		B		C
Medals & Prizes!	1	9	+	9	=	
	2	6	+	7	=	
Make Antonio by setting a Personal Best, reaching your goal, and winning a medal.	3	6	+	7	=	
	4	7	+	11	=	
ANT 20	5	6	+	1	=	
	6	7	+	2	=	
Gold 30	7	6	+	8	=	
	8	12	+	11	=	
Silver 50	9	7	+	3	=	
	10	10	+	12	=	
Bronze 01:30	11	7	+	12	=	
Hand Speed	12	10	+	9	=	
Bonus	13	12	+	12	=	
Total Time	14	0	+	9	=	
ANTONIO	15	11	+	1	=	
P * B GOAL	16	1	+	9	=	
	17	7	+	5	=	
	18	7	+	1	=	
	19	12	+	6	=	
	20	7	+	1	=	

Copyright Alexander F.L. Newberry

34

| Ex. | 32 | Skill Set Medley | | | | Date |

Circle your goal. Fill in the numbers iin the boxes marked 'X'. Check your answers. If you write the date and get 100% you get a 5 second bonus!

Question	A		B		C
	X	+	10	=	20
	0	+	X	=	20
	9	+	0	=	X
	9	+	X	=	20
	X	+	8	=	20
	14	+	X	=	20
	5	+	1	=	X
	8	+	X	=	20
	X	+	6	=	20
	7	+	X	=	20
	0	+	4	=	X
	1	+	X	=	20
	X	+	6	=	20
	7	+	X	=	20
	0	+	7	=	X
	6	+	X	=	20
	X	+	9	=	20
	5	+	X	=	20
	9	+	0	=	X
	9	+	X	=	20

Medals & Prizes!

Make Antonio by setting a Personal Best, reaching your goal, and winning a medal.

20	ANT
30	Gold
50	Silver
01:30	Bronze
	Hand Speed
	Bonus
	Total Time

ANTONIO

P * B   GOAL

Copyright Alexander F.L. Newberry

Circle your goal. Fill in the numbers in the 'A' Column. If you write the date and get 100% you get a 5 second bonus!

Medals & Prizes!

Make Antonio by setting a Personal Best, reaching your goal, and winning a medal.

ANT	20
Gold	30
Silver	50
Bronze	01:30
Hand Speed	
Bonus	
Total Time	

ANTONIO

P * B   GOAL

Question	A		B		C
	x	+	5	=	20
	x	+	17	=	20
	x	+	18	=	20
	x	+	8	=	20
	x	+	13	=	20
	x	+	19	=	20
	x	+	6	=	20
	x	+	19	=	20
	x	+	20	=	20
	x	+	7	=	20
	x	+	7	=	20
	x	+	18	=	20
	x	+	15	=	20
	x	+	4	=	20
	x	+	0	=	20
	x	+	3	=	20
	x	+	13	=	20
	x	+	16	=	20
	x	+	20	=	20
	x	+	15	=	20

Skill Set B

Circle your goal. Fill in the numbers in the 'B' Column. If you write the date and get 100% you get a 5 second bonus!

Question	A		B		C
	16	+	x	=	20
	2	+	x	=	20
	17	+	x	=	20
	13	+	x	=	20
	0	+	x	=	20
	6	+	x	=	20
	19	+	x	=	20
	20	+	x	=	20
	7	+	x	=	20
	10	+	x	=	20
	16	+	x	=	20
	4	+	x	=	20
	14	+	x	=	20
	11	+	x	=	20
	14	+	x	=	20
	1	+	x	=	20
	9	+	x	=	20
	0	+	x	=	20
	2	+	x	=	20
	6	+	x	=	20

Medals & Prizes!

Make Antonio by setting a Personal Best, reaching your goal, and winning a medal.

20	ANT
30	Gold
50	Silver
01:30	Bronze
	Hand Speed
	Bonus
	Total Time

ANTONIO

P * B   GOAL

Circle your goal. Fill in the numbers in the 'C' Column. Check your answers. If you write the date and get 100% you get a 5 second bonus!

Medals & Prizes!

Make Antonio by setting a Personal Best, reaching your goal, and winning a medal.

ANT	20
Gold	30
Silver	50
Bronze	01:30
Hand Speed	
Bonus	
Total Time	

ANTONIO

P * B   GOAL

Question	A		B		C
1	10	+	5	=	x
2	11	+	4	=	x
3	2	+	4	=	x
4	4	+	6	=	x
5	3	+	5	=	x
6	5	+	9	=	x
7	2	+	10	=	x
8	6	+	3	=	x
9	4	+	9	=	x
10	7	+	12	=	x
11	6	+	12	=	x
12	5	+	8	=	x
13	0	+	12	=	x
14	4	+	8	=	x
15	5	+	8	=	x
16	6	+	0	=	x
17	11	+	4	=	x
18	7	+	9	=	x
19	8	+	1	=	x
20	7	+	2	=	x

Circle your goal. Fill in the numbers iin the boxes marked 'X'. Check your answers. If you write the date and get 100% you get a 5 second bonus!

Question	A		B		C
	X	+	1	=	20
	14	+	X	=	20
	8	+	12	=	X
	12	+	X	=	20
	X	+	9	=	20
	6	+	X	=	20
	4	+	5	=	X
	9	+	X	=	20
	X	+	10	=	20
	11	+	X	=	20
	6	+	6	=	X
	9	+	X	=	20
	X	+	1	=	20
	12	+	X	=	20
	10	+	2	=	X
	1	+	X	=	20
	X	+	16	=	20
	11	+	X	=	20
	5	+	10	=	X
	16	+	X	=	20

Medals & Prizes!

Make Antonio by setting a Personal Best, reaching your goal, and winning a medal.

20	ANT
30	Gold
50	Silver
01:30	Bronze
	Hand Speed
	Bonus
	Total Time

ANTONIO

P * B   GOAL

Skill Set A

Ex. | 37

Circle your goal. Fill in the numbers in the 'A' Column. If you write the date and get 100% you get a 5 second bonus!

Medals & Prizes!

Make Antonio by setting a Personal Best, reaching your goal, and winning a medal.

ANT	20
Gold	30
Silver	50
Bronze	01:30
Hand Speed	
Bonus	
Total Time	

ANTONIO
P * B   GOAL

Question	A		B		C
	x	+	1	=	20
	x	+	6	=	20
	x	+	1	=	20
	x	+	4	=	20
	x	+	1	=	20
	x	+	14	=	20
	x	+	13	=	20
	x	+	7	=	20
	x	+	9	=	20
10	x	+	16	=	20
11	x	+	18	=	20
12	x	+	17	=	20
13	x	+	0	=	20
14	x	+	17	=	20
15	x	+	2	=	20
16	x	+	11	=	20
17	x	+	20	=	20
18	x	+	8	=	20
19	x	+	19	=	20
20	x	+	4	=	20

Circle your goal. Fill in the numbers in the 'B' Column. If you write the date and get 100% you get a 5 second bonus!

Question	A		B		C	Medals & Prizes!	
	4	+	x	=	20	Make Antonio by setting a Personal Best, reaching your goal, and winning a medal.	
	4	+	x	=	20		
	1	+	x	=	20	20	ANT
	14	+	x	=	20		
	18	+	x	=	20	30	Gold
	2	+	x	=	20		
	0	+	x	=	20	50	Silver
	6	+	x	=	20		
	8	+	x	=	20	01:30	Bronze
	2	+	x	=	20		
	7	+	x	=	20		Hand Speed
	6	+	x	=	20		Bonus
	0	+	x	=	20		Total Time
	5	+	x	=	20	ANTONIO	
	5	+	x	=	20	P * B	GOAL
	20	+	x	=	20		
	18	+	x	=	20		
	15	+	x	=	20		
	3	+	x	=	20		
	13	+	x	=	20		

| | Date | | Skill Set C | | | Ex. | 39 |

Skill Set C

Ex. 39

Circle your goal. Fill in the numbers in the 'C' Column. Check your answers. If you write the date and get 100% you get a 5 second bonus!

Question	A		B		C
1	10	+	3	=	X
2	2	+	6	=	X
3	0	+	5	=	X
4	0	+	4	=	X
5	0	+	7	=	X
6	3	+	4	=	X
7	3	+	6	=	X
8	6	+	1	=	X
9	10	+	8	=	X
10	9	+	8	=	X
11	12	+	3	=	X
12	5	+	8	=	X
13	12	+	6	=	X
14	4	+	1	=	X
15	9	+	5	=	X
16	6	+	11	=	X
17	1	+	12	=	X
18	5	+	0	=	X
19	10	+	2	=	X
20	4	+	11	=	X

Medals & Prizes!

Make Antonio by setting a Personal Best, reaching your goal, and winning a medal.

ANT	20
Gold	30
Silver	50
Bronze	01:30
Hand Speed	
Bonus	
Total Time	

ANTONIO

| P * B | GOAL |

Copyright Alexander F.L. Newberry

Skill Set Medley

Date

Circle your goal. Fill in the numbers iin the boxes marked 'X'. Check your answers. If you write the date and get 100% you get a 5 second bonus!

Question	A		B		C
	X	+	18	=	20
	7	+	X	=	20
	6	+	8	=	X
	18	+	X	=	20
	X	+	4	=	20
	8	+	X	=	20
	4	+	5	=	X
	4	+	X	=	20
	X	+	9	=	20
	5	+	X	=	20
	0	+	0	=	X
	0	+	X	=	20
	X	+	2	=	20
	6	+	X	=	20
	11	+	2	=	X
	2	+	X	=	20
	X	+	19	=	20
	16	+	X	=	20
	4	+	3	=	X
	19	+	X	=	20

Medals & Prizes!

Make Antonio by setting a Personal Best, reaching your goal, and winning a medal.

20	ANT
30	Gold
50	Silver
01:30	Bronze
	Hand Speed
	Bonus
	Total Time

ANTONIO

P * B   GOAL

Antonio Set Speed Graph

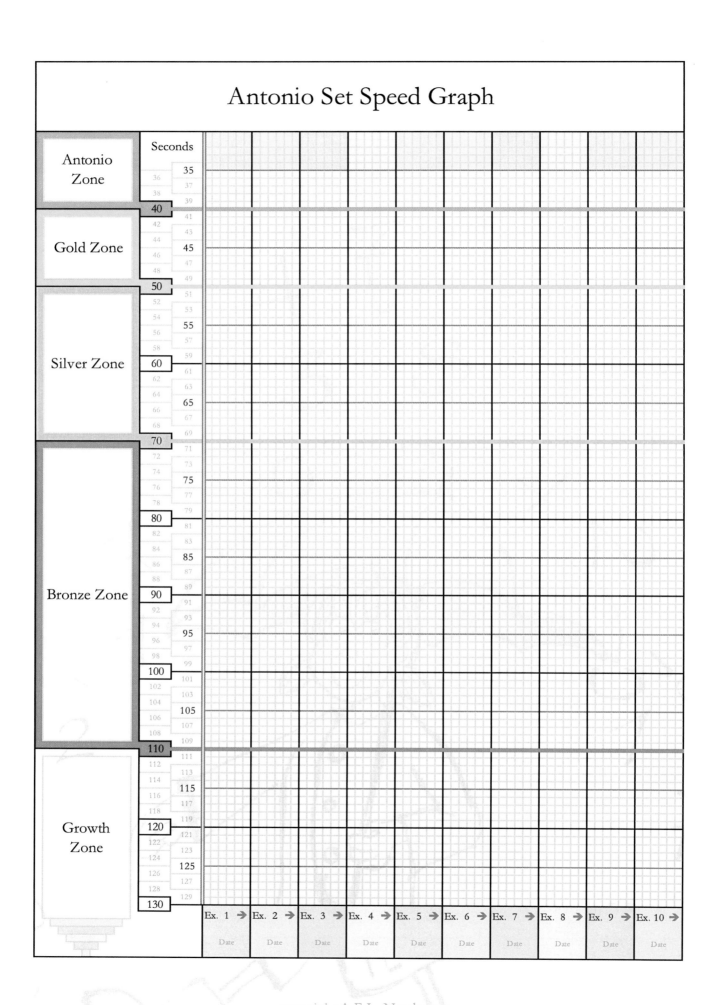

| | Seconds | | | Ex. 1 → | Ex. 2 → | Ex. 3 → | Ex. 4 → | Ex. 5 → | Ex. 6 → | Ex. 7 → | Ex. 8 → | Ex. 9 → | Ex. 10 → |

Antonio Zone

Gold Zone

Silver Zone

Bronze Zone

Growth Zone

Seconds
35
36
37
38
39
40
41
42
43
44
45
46
47
48
49
50
51
52
53
54
55
56
57
58
59
60
61
62
63
64
65
66
67
68
69
70
71
72
73
74
75
76
77
78
79
80
81
82
83
84
85
86
87
88
89
90
91
92
93
94
95
96
97
98
99
100
101
102
103
104
105
106
107
108
109
110
111
112
113
114
115
116
117
118
119
120
121
122
123
124
125
126
127
128
129
130

Ex. 1 → Date
Ex. 2 → Date
Ex. 3 → Date
Ex. 4 → Date
Ex. 5 → Date
Ex. 6 → Date
Ex. 7 → Date
Ex. 8 → Date
Ex. 9 → Date
Ex. 10 → Date

Plot A Type to A Type, B Type to B Type, C Type to C Type, Medley to Medley.

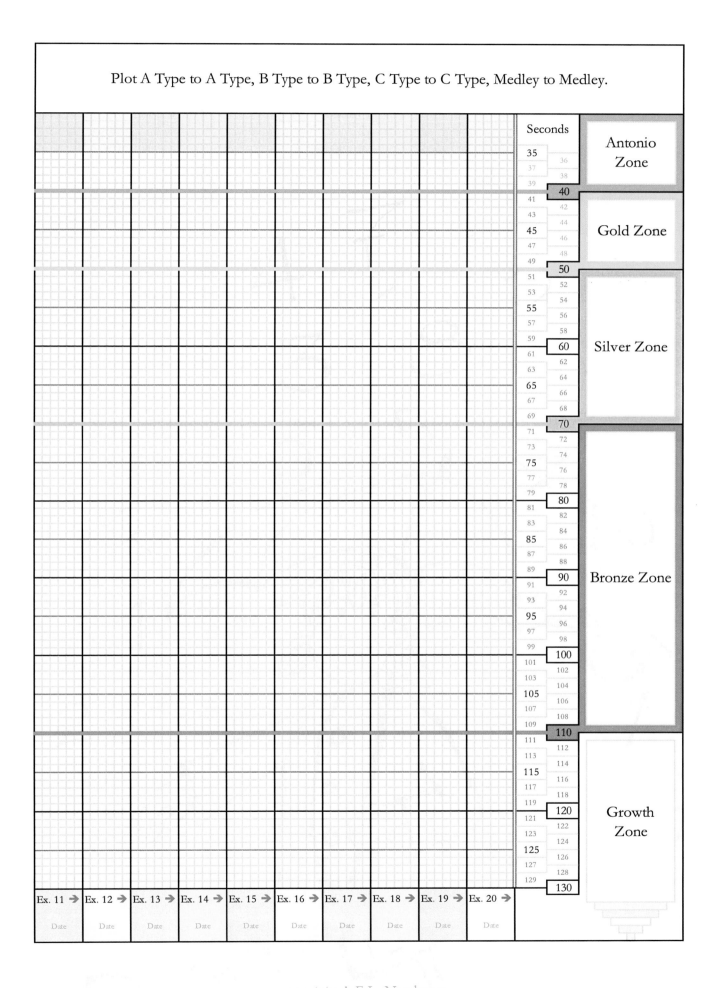

Seconds	Zone
35	Antonio Zone
36	
37	
38	
39	
40	
41	Gold Zone
42	
43	
44	
45	
46	
47	
48	
49	
50	
51	Silver Zone
52	
53	
54	
55	
56	
57	
58	
59	
60	
61	
62	
63	
64	
65	
66	
67	
68	
69	
70	
71	Bronze Zone
72	
...	

Ex. 11 ➔ Ex. 12 ➔ Ex. 13 ➔ Ex. 14 ➔ Ex. 15 ➔ Ex. 16 ➔ Ex. 17 ➔ Ex. 18 ➔ Ex. 19 ➔ Ex. 20 ➔

Date   Date   Date   Date   Date   Date   Date   Date   Date   Date

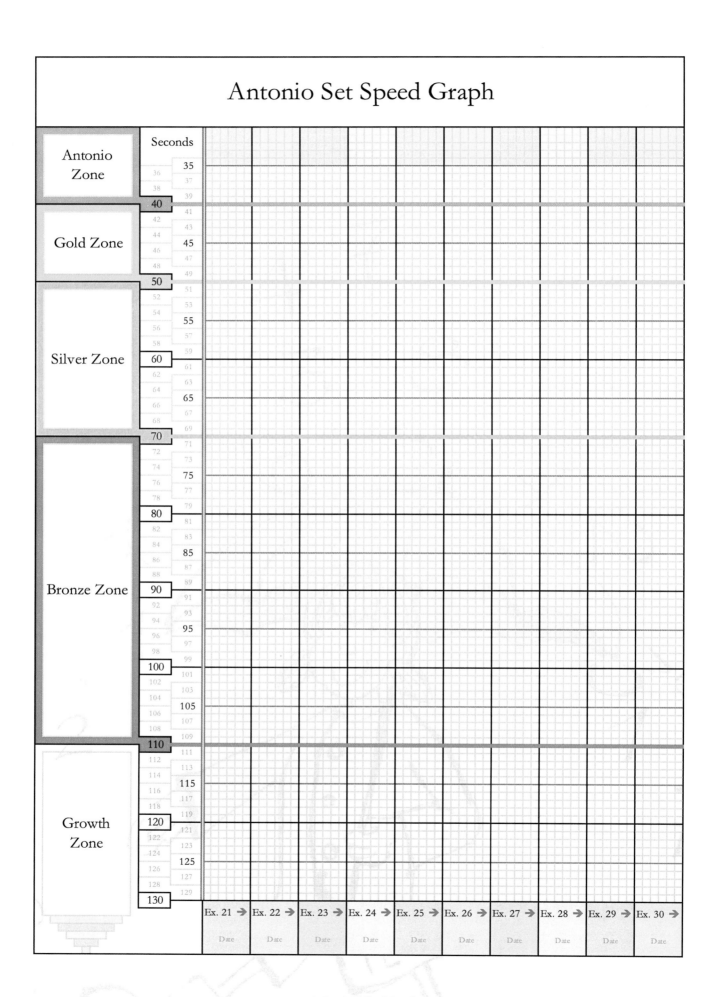

Antonio Set Speed Graph

Zone	Seconds
Antonio Zone	35, 36, 37, 38, 39, 40
Gold Zone	41, 42, 43, 44, 45, 46, 47, 48, 49, 50
Silver Zone	51, 52, 53, 54, 55, 56, 57, 58, 59, 60, 61, 62, 63, 64, 65, 66, 67, 68, 69, 70
Bronze Zone	71, 72, 73, 74, 75, 76, 77, 78, 79, 80, 81, 82, 83, 84, 85, 86, 87, 88, 89, 90, 91, 92, 93, 94, 95, 96, 97, 98, 99, 100, 101, 102, 103, 104, 105, 106, 107, 108, 109, 110
Growth Zone	111, 112, 113, 114, 115, 116, 117, 118, 119, 120, 121, 122, 123, 124, 125, 126, 127, 128, 129, 130

Ex. 21 →	Ex. 22 →	Ex. 23 →	Ex. 24 →	Ex. 25 →	Ex. 26 →	Ex. 27 →	Ex. 28 →	Ex. 29 →	Ex. 30 →
Date	Date	Date	Date	Date	Date	Date	Date	Date	Date

Plot A Type to A Type, B Type to B Type, C Type to C Type, Medley to Medley.

	Seconds	
	35	Antonio Zone
	36	
	37	
	38	
	39	
	40	
	41	Gold Zone
	42	
	43	
	44	
	45	
	46	
	47	
	48	
	49	
	50	
	51	Silver Zone
	52	
	53	
	54	
	55	
	56	
	57	
	58	
	59	
	60	
	61	
	62	
	63	
	64	
	65	
	66	
	67	
	68	
	69	
	70	
	71	Bronze Zone
	72	
	73	
	74	
	75	
	76	
	77	
	78	
	79	
	80	
	81	
	82	
	83	
	84	
	85	
	86	
	87	
	88	
	89	
	90	
	91	
	92	
	93	
	94	
	95	
	96	
	97	
	98	
	99	
	100	
	101	
	102	
	103	
	104	
	105	
	106	
	107	
	108	
	109	
	110	
	111	Growth Zone
	112	
	113	
	114	
	115	
	116	
	117	
	118	
	119	
	120	
	121	
	122	
	123	
	124	
	125	
	126	
	127	
	128	
	129	
	130	

Ex. 31 → Ex. 32 → Ex. 33 → Ex. 34 → Ex. 35 → Ex. 36 → Ex. 37 → Ex. 38 → Ex. 39 → Ex. 40 →

Date Date Date Date Date Date Date Date Date Date

Numberella

A Little Maths | A Little Luck | A Lot Of Fun

"Makes kids of all abilities beg to do math."

Dr. April De Gennaro,
Georgia (USA) Teacher of the Year

- ✔ US and UK syllabus supporting
- ✔ Data proven
- ✔ Included in 'Gifted' curriculum (US)
- ✔ SEND ratified (UK & US)
- ✔ Data proven to improve exam results
- ✔ 100% 5* Amazon Reviews
- ✔ Little to no lesson preparation
- ✔ Free league creation software

Mathematics

Motivational Brain Training Books

Tiger Addition

Building Better Brains

"we have moved to a wholesale shift in Moss's school performance."

Jason Mitra
Parent, London, 2018

- ✔ 100% increase processing speed
- ✔ Data proven
- ✔ 100% improve concentration stamina
- ✔ Helps create growth mindset
- ✔ Improves exam results
- ✔ Little to no preparation
- ✔ Accelerates arithmetic of markers
- ✔ Includes x66 big stickers!

- ✔ The Year 2098 : Earth underwater
- ✔ Flood barriers managed by AI
- ✔ Aliens entering via worm holes
- ✔ Plots to enslave humanity
- ✔ Heroes needing help
- ✔ Questions to answer
- ✔ Missions to complete
- ✔ Prizes to win

"My kids are loving the escape room!! Thankyou!"

Avis Whitt, Lanier Middle School, Georgia USA

Escape Rooms

The Adventures of Numberella & Friends

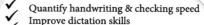

- ✔ Quantify handwriting & checking speed
- ✔ Improve dictation skills
- ✔ Associate words by poetical potential
- ✔ Build a story idea database
- ✔ Flip spelling into a scoring opportunity
- ✔ Learn to think outside the box
- ✔ Evolve to access high level English
- ✔ Includes x66 big stickers

"AJ was awarded a Head Master's Good Show for his English!"

Parent, London 2019

English Evolution

Building Better Brains

English

Motivational Creative Accelerator Books